Color Me Peaceful

This Book Belongs to:

_____

- -

_____

Copyrights:

WHY CURSIVE?

-Brain Function

"Putting pen to paper stimulates the brain like nothing else, even in this age of e-mails, texts and tweets. In fact, learning to write in cursive is shown to improve brain development in the areas of thinking, language and working memory. Cursive handwriting stimulates brain synapses and synchronicity between the left and right hemispheres, something absent from printing and typing." Suzanne Baruch Asherson

-Better Learning

Studies have even shown that students who wrote essays in cursive scored higher on SATs.

-Memorization

Furthermore. studies have shown that when you write something down on paper with a pen or pencil, you create thousands more brain connections and memorize much more quickly, easily, and permanently.

-Beauty and connection

But beyond that, the art of beautiful handwriting and how special it is to receive a handwritten letter from someone need not be lost! There is something truly special and heartwarming about holding in your hand a note that the person who sent it also held in their hand and took the time to write legibly and beautifully.

TIPS for improving Cursive Writing:

1. Remember **why** you want to do it and keep the end in mind!

2. Be **patient** with the learning process! You CAN do it—just be consistent in your practicing!

3. **Set a time and place** each day to do one page. It is set up so that you do 1 practice page Monday-Thursday and then on Friday, you write and color the final page which will be a **beautiful, frameable picture!**

4. Each day, spend a few minutes **practicing a few letters** and the stroke order in the front of the book before going to the practice page.

5. **Relax your hand** as much as possible to minimize fatigue and a relaxed hand makes smoother, more flowing strokes.

6. **Make the switch!** whenever you write—even just taking notes—write in cursive. Everyday life gives you more opportunities to practice.

7. The last coloring page makes a **nice gift!** Frame it and Voila!

Practicing the letters

Aa Aa Aa Aa Aa
Aa Aa Aa Aa Aa

Bb Bb Bb Bb Bb
Bb Bb Bb Bb Bb

Cc Cc Cc Cc
Cc Cc Cc Cc

Dd Dd Dd Dd Dd
Dd Dd Dd Dd Dd

Ee Ee Ee Ee
Ee Ee Ee Ee

Ff Ff Ff Ff Ff
Ff Ff Ff Ff Ff

Gg Gg Gg Gg Gg
Gg Gg Gg Gg Gg

Practicing the letters

Practicing the letters

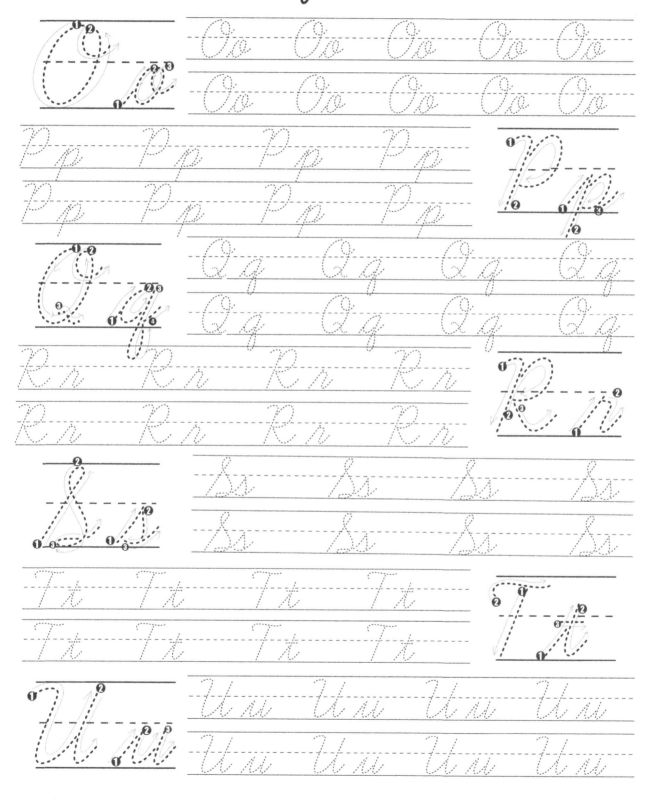

Practicing the letters

Practice and memorization #1

John 14:27

Peace I   Peace I

leave with   leave with

you. My   you. My

peace I   peace I

give you.   give you.

I do not   I do not

Peace I leave with you, My

peace I give you. I do not

give to you as the world gives.

Do not let your hearts be

troubled and do not be afraid. KJV

Practice and memorization #2

John 14:27

give to you   give to you

as the   as the

world gives.   world gives.

Do not   Do not

let your   let your

hearts be   hearts be

Peace I leave with you, My

peace I give you. I do not

give to you as the world gives.

Do not let your hearts be

troubled and do not be afraid.

Practice and memorization #3

John 14:27

troubled   troubled

and do   and do

not be   not be

afraid.   afraid.

John 14:27

Peace I leave with you. My

peace I give you. I do not

give to you as the world gives.

Do not let your hearts be

troubled and do not be afraid.

John 14:27

Practice and memorization # 4

John 14:27

Peace I leave with you. My
peace I give you. I do not
give to you as the world gives.
Do not let your hearts be
troubled and do not be afraid.

John 14:27

Peace I leave with you. My
peace I give you. I do not
give to you as the world gives.
Do not let your hearts be
troubled and do not be afraid.

"Peace I leave with you, My peace I give to you. I do not give to you as the world gives.

Do not let your hearts be troubled, and do not be afraid."
John 14:27 KJV

Left intentionally blank to not show through

Practice and memorization #1

John 16:33

I have   I have

said these   said these

things   things

to you   to you

that in me   that in me

"I have said these things to you,

that in me you may have peace.

In the world you will have

tribulation. But take heart, I

have overcome the world."

John 16:33 ESV

Practice and memorization #2

John 16:33

you may   you may

have peace   have peace

In the world   In the world

you will have

tribulation

"I have said these things to you,

that in me you may have peace.

In the world you will have

tribulation. But take heart, I

have overcome the world."

John 16:33   John 16:33   ESV

Practice and memorization # 3

John 16:33

But take   But take

heart   heart   heart

I have   I have

overcome   overcome

the world   the world

"I have said these things to you,

that in me you may have peace.

In the world you will have

tribulation. But take heart, I

have overcome the world."

John 16:33   John 16:33   ESV

Practice and memorization # 4

John 16:33

"I have said these things to you,
that in me you may have peace.
In the world you will have
tribulation. But take heart,
I have overcome the world."

"I have said these things to you,
that in me you may have peace.
In the world you will have
tribulation. But take heart,
I have overcome the world."

John 16:33   John 16:33   ESV

"I have said these things to you, that in me you may have peace.

In the world you will have tribulation. But take heart; I have overcome the world." John 16:33 ESV

Left intentionally blank to not show through

Practice and memorization #1

Jeremiah 29:11

For I   For I   For I

know   know   know

the plans   the plans

that I   that I   that I

have for   have for

"For I know the plans that I

have for you declares the Lord

plans to prosper you and not

to harm you, plans to give

you hope and a future."

Jeremiah 29:11

Practice and memorization #2

Jeremiah 29:11

you   you   you

declares   declares   declares

the Lord   the Lord

plans to   plans to

prosper   prosper

"For I know the plans that I
have for you declares the Lord
plans to prosper you and not
to harm you, plans to give
you hope and a future."
Jeremiah 29:11 Jeremiah 29:11 NIV

Practice and memorization # 3

Jeremiah 29:11

harm you   harm you

plans to   plans to

prosper   prosper

hope   hope   hope

future   future   future

For I know the plans that I

have for you declares the Lord

plans to prosper you and not

to harm you, plans to give

you hope and a future.

Jeremiah 29:11 Jeremiah 29:11 NIV

Practice and memorization # 4

Jeremiah 29:11

"For I know the plans that I have for you declares the Lord plans to prosper you and not to harm you, plans to give you hope and a future."

"For I know the plans that I have for you declares the Lord plans to prosper you and not to harm you, plans to give you hope and a future."

Jeremiah 29:11 Jeremiah 29:11 NIV

"For I know the plans that I have for you," declares the Lord,

"plans to prosper you and not to harm you, plans to give you hope and a future." Jeremiah 29:11 NIV

Left intentionally blank to not show through

Practice and memorization # 1

Psalm 29:11

The   The   The

Lord   Lord   Lord

gives   gives   gives

his   his   his

people   people   people

strength   strength

The Lord   The Lord

blesses   blesses   blesses

"The Lord gives his people

strength. The Lord blesses them

with peace." Psalm 29:11

Practice and memorization #2

Psalm 29:11

them   them   them

with   with   with

peace   peace   peace

Psalm 29:11   Psalm 29:11

strength   strength

"The Lord gives his people

strength. The Lord blesses them

with peace."   Psalm 29:11   NLT

"The Lord gives his people

strength. The Lord blesses them

with peace."   Psalm 29:11   NLT

Practice and memorization #3

Psalm 29:11

The Lord gives his people

The Lord gives his people

strength. The Lord blesses

strength. The Lord blesses

them with peace."

them with peace."

The Lord gives his people

The Lord gives his people

strength. The Lord blesses them

with peace." Psalm 29:11

Psalm 29:11 Psalm 29:11

Practice and memorization #4

Psalm 29:11

"The Lord gives his people strength. The Lord blesses them with peace."

Psalm 29:11   Psalm 29:11

"The Lord gives his people strength. The Lord blesses them with peace."

Psalm 29:11   Psalm 29:11

"The Lord gives his people strength. The Lord blesses them with peace."   Psalm 29:11

NLT

"The Lord gives his people strength.

The Lord blesses them with peace." Psalm 29:11 NLT

Left intentionally blank to not show through

Practice and memorization #1

Isaiah 26:3

You   You   You

will   will   will

keep   keep   keep

them   them   them

in   in   in   in

perfect   perfect   perfect

"You will keep them in perfect

You will keep them in perfect

peace, whose mind is stayed on

you because they trust in you."

Isaiah 26:3   Isaiah 26:3   NKJV

Practice and memorization #2

Isaiah 26:3

peace   peace   peace

whose   whose   whose

mind   mind   mind

is   is   is   is

stayed   stayed   stayed

on   on   on   on

"peace, whose mind is stayed on

You will keep them in perfect

peace, whose mind is stayed on

you because they trust in You."

Isaiah 26:3   Isaiah 26:3

NKJV

Practice and memorization #3

Isaiah 26:3

you   you   you

because   because

they   they   they

trust   trust   trust

in   in   in   in

you   you   you

Isaiah 26:3   Isaiah 26:3

"You will keep them in perfect

peace, whose mind is stayed on

you because they trust in you."

Isaiah 26:3   Isaiah 26:3

Practice and memorization #4

Isaiah 26:3

"You will keep them in perfect peace, whose mind is stayed on you because they trust in you."

You will keep them in perfect peace, whose mind is stayed on you because they trust in you.

Isaiah 26:3   Isaiah 26:3

"You will keep them in perfect peace, whose mind is stayed on you because they trust in you."

Isaiah 26:3   Isaiah 26:3

NKJV

"You will keep them in perfect peace, whose mind is stayed on You,

because they trust in You." Isaiah 26:3 NKJV

Left intentionally blank to not show through

Oh   Oh

God   God   God

my   my   my

heart   heart   heart

Left intentionally blank to not show through.

is   is   is   is

quiet   quiet   quiet

and   and   and

confident   confident   confident

Oh God my heart is quiet
and confident. No wonder I
can sing Your praises! TPT

Practice and memorization #3

Proverbs 3:17

Wisdom. Wisdom.

"Her ways are pleasant,

"Her ways are pleasant,

and all her paths, peaceful.

and all her paths, peaceful.

Proverbs 3:17 Proverbs 3:17

"Her ways are pleasant,

and all her paths, peaceful.

"Her ways are pleasant, and

all her paths, peaceful."

Proverbs 3:17 HCSB

Practice and memorization #4

Proverbs 3:17

Wisdom. Wisdom.

"Her ways are pleasant, and all her paths, peaceful."

Proverbs 3:17

Wisdom. Wisdom.

"Her ways are pleasant, and all her paths, peaceful."

Wisdom. Wisdom.

"Her ways are pleasant, and all her paths, peaceful."

Proverbs 3:17

HCSB

Practice and memorization #2

Proverbs 3:17

peaceful   peaceful

Wisdom.   Wisdom.

Her ways   Her ways

are pleasant,   are pleasant,

and all her paths,

peaceful.   peaceful.

Proverbs 3:17

Wisdom.   Wisdom.

"Her ways are pleasant, and

all her paths, peaceful."

Proverbs 3:17

HCSB

Wisdom

"Her ways are pleasant, and all her paths, peaceful."

Proverbs 3:17 HCSB

Practice and memorization #1

Oh Oh

God God God

my my my

heart heart heart

is is is is

quiet quiet quiet

and and and

confident confident confident

Oh God, my heart is quiet
and confident. No wonder I
can sing Your praises! TPT

Psalm 57:7

No   No   No
wonder   wonder
I   I   I   I
can   can   can
sing   sing   sing
Your   Your   Your
praises!   praises!
Psalm 57:7
Oh God, my heart is quiet
and confident. No wonder I
can sing Your praises! TPT

Practice and memorization #3

Psalm 57:7

Oh God, my heart is quiet
and confident. No wonder I
can sing Your praises!

Psalm 57:7

Oh God, my heart is quiet
and confident. No wonder I
can sing Your praises!

TPT

Practice and memorization #4

Psalm 57:7

Oh God, my heart is quiet and confident. No wonder I can sing Your praises!

Psalm 57:7

Oh God, my heart is quiet and confident. No wonder I can sing Your praises! TPT

"Oh God, my heart is quiet and confident.

No wonder I can sing Your praises!" ᴛᴘᴛ

Psalm 57:7

Left intentionally blank to not show through

Practice and memorization #1

1 Peter 5:6-7

Humble   Humble

yourself   yourself

under the   under the

mighty   mighty

hand   hand   hand

"Humble yourselves, therefore,

under the mighty hand of

God that He may exalt you

at the proper time, casting

all your cares upon Him,

because He cares about you." CSB

Practice and memorization #2

1 Peter 5:6-7

of God   of God   of God

that He   that He   that He

may   may   may

exalt   exalt   exalt

you at   you at   you at

"Humble yourselves, therefore,

under the mighty hand of

God that He may exalt you

at the proper time, casting

all your cares upon Him,

because He cares about you." CSB

Practice and memorization #3

1 Peter 5:6-7

the proper   the proper

time   time   time

casting   casting

all your   all your

cares   cares   cares

"Humble yourselves, therefore,

under the mighty hand of

God that He may exalt you

at the proper time, casting

all your cares upon Him,

because He cares about you." CSB

1 Peter 5:6-7

upon   upon   upon

Him   Him   Him

because   because

He cares   He cares

for you.   for you.

"Humble yourselves, therefore,

under the mighty hand of

God that He may exalt you

at the proper time, casting

all your cares upon Him,

because He cares about you."   CSB

"Humble yourselves, therefore, under mighty hand of God, so that he may exalt you at the proper time,

casting all your cares on Him, because He cares about you."
1 Peter 5:6-7 CSB

Left intentionally blank to not show through

Practice and memorization # 1

Phil. 4:7

And   And   And

the   the   the

peace   peace

of   of   of

God   God   God

Phil. 4:7

"And the peace of God,

which surpasses all

understanding will guard your

hearts and your minds

in Christ Jesus." BSB

Practice and memorization # 2

Phil. 4:7

which   which

surpasses   surpasses

all   all   all

understanding

understanding

will   will   will

"And the peace of God,

which surpasses all

understanding will guard your

hearts and your minds

in Christ Jesus." BSB

Practice and memorization # 3

Phil. 4:7

guard   guard   guard

your   your   your

hearts   hearts   hearts

and your   and your

minds   minds   minds

Phil. 4:7   Phil. 4:7

"And the peace of God,

which surpasses all

understanding will guard your

hearts and your minds

in Christ Jesus." BSB

Practice and memorization #4

Phil. 4:7

in   in   in   in

Christ   Christ

Jesus   Jesus

surpasses all

understanding

Phil. 4:7   Phil. 4:7

"And the peace of God,

which surpasses all

understanding will guard your

hearts and your minds

in Christ Jesus." BSB

"And the peace of God, which
surpasses all understanding,

Phil. 4:7

will guard your hearts and
your minds in Christ Jesus."

BSB

Left intentionally blank to not show through

Practice and memorization #1

Psalm 4:8

In   In   In

peace   peace   peace

I   I   I

will   will   will

both   both   both

lie   lie   lie

down   down   down

and   and   and

"In peace I will both lie down

and sleep for you alone, O Lord,

make me dwell in safety." NASB

Practice and memorization #2

Psalm 4:8

sleep   sleep   sleep

for   for   for

You   You   You

alone,   alone,   alone,

O   O   O   O

Lord,   Lord,   Lord,

make   make   make

me   me   me

"In peace I will both lie down

and sleep for you alone, O Lord,

make me dwell in safety." NASB

Practice and memorization #3

Psalm 4:8

dwell   dwell   dwell

in   in   in   in

safety   safety

Psalm 4:8

"In peace I will both lie down

and sleep for you alone, O Lord,

make me dwell in safety."

"In peace I will both lie down

and sleep for you alone, O Lord,

make me dwell in safety." NASB

Psalm 4:8

Practice and memorization #4

Psalm 4:8

"In peace I will both lie down
and sleep for you alone, O Lord,
make me dwell in safety."

Psalm 4:8

"In peace I will both lie down
and sleep for you alone, O Lord,
make me dwell in safety."

Psalm 4:8

"In peace I will both lie down
and sleep for you alone, O Lord,
make me dwell in safety." NASB

"In peace I with both
lie down and sleep,
Psalm 4:8

For You alone, O Lord,
make me dwell in safety." nasb

Left intentionally blank to not show through

"The Lord bless you
and keep you;
The Lord make his face
shine on you and be
gracious to you;
The Lord lift up his
countenance upon you
and give you peace."
Numbers 6:24-26 NAS

If you liked this book,
(we hope it was a blessing!)
please check out our other titles at our
Amazon Author Central Page and our
website!
www.WonderfulWorldPress.net

Wonderful World
PRESS
LIVE, LOVE, LEARN

Made in the USA
Coppell, TX
16 January 2024